Biology for the Grammar Stage

Student Workbook

Biology for the Grammar Stage Student Workbook

Updated Edition, 2nd Printing

Email: support@elementalscience.com

ISBN # 978-1-935614-29-6

Printed in the USA for worldwide distribution
Pictures by Paige Hudson and Erin Simons (One Line Design)

For more copies write to:
Elemental Science
PO Box 79
Niceville, FL 32588
support@elementalscience.com

Copyright Policy

Biology for the Grammar Stage Student Workbook

Biology for the Grammar Stage

Animals Unit

Animal Diet Chart

Herbivore	Omnivore	Carnivore

Animal Diet Chart

Herbivore	Omnivore	Carnivore

Desert

Grassland

Rainforest

Lab Report: My Habitat Diorama

What I Learned

Woodlands

Arctic

Camouflage

Lab Report: Camouflage

Our Tools

Our Method

What it looked like

Our Outcome

Our Insight

Lion

Cheetah

Elephant

Lab Report: Cat's Eyes

Our Tools

Our Method

Our Outcome

Our Insight

Zebra

Hippo

Fox

Lab Report: Blending

Our Tools

Our Method

Our Outcome

Our Insight

Giraffe

Camel

Deer

Lab Report: Camels

Our Tools

Our Method

What it looked like

Our Outcome

Our Insight

Panda

Polar Bear

Chimpanzee

Lab Report: Polar Bear

Our Tools

Our Method

Our Outcome

	Moved First	Moved Faster
Uncovered Can		
Covered Can		

Our Insight

Kangaroo

Koala

Beaver

Lab Report: Ear Size

Our Tools

______________________ ______________________

______________________ ______________________

Our Method

____

____

____

____

Our Outcome

	Distance when I could no longer hear
Regular Hearing	
Hearing with a Cup	

____

____

____

____

Our Insight

____

____

____

____

____

Armadillo

Skunk

Rabbit

Lab Report: Warm-blooded

Our Tools

Our Method

Our Outcome

Glass #1	
Initial Temperature	
Temperature after cooling in water	
Glass #2	
Initial Temperature	
Temperature after cooling in the freezer	

Our Insight

Walrus

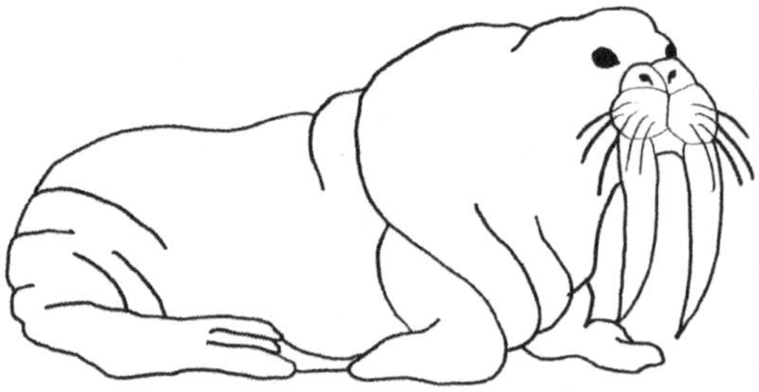

Whale

Dolphin

Lab Report: Tangled

Our Tools

Our Method

Our Outcome

Our Insight

Goat

Cow

Pig

Lab Report: Hairy

Our Tools

Our Method

Our Outcome

Glass Jar Outside the Box	
Initial Temperature	
Temperature after 15 minutes	
Glass Jar in the Box	
Initial Temperature	
Temperature after 15 minutes	

Our Insight

Eagle

Owl

Parrot

Lab Report: Soda Bottle Bird Feeder

What I Learned

Penguin

Chicken

Duck

Lab Report: Oily Feathers

Our Tools

Our Method

Our Outcome

Our Insight

Swan

Swallow

Hummingbird

Lab Report: Lift Off

Our Tools

Our Method

Our Outcome

Our Insight

Flamingo

Peacock

Ostrich

Lab Report: Naked Egg

Our Tools

Our Method

What Happened	
	Size in cm
Initial	
Final	

Our Outcome

Initial Appearance

Appearance on Day 2

Appearance on Day 3

Our Insight

Chameleon

Iguana

Rattlesnake

Lab Report: Ground Temperature

Our Tools

Our Method

Our Outcome

On top of the ground	
Initial Temperature	
Temperature after 5 minutes	
Buried in the ground	
Initial Temperature	
Temperature after 5 minutes	

Our Insight

Alligator

Turtle

Frog

Lab Report: Life Cycle of a Frog

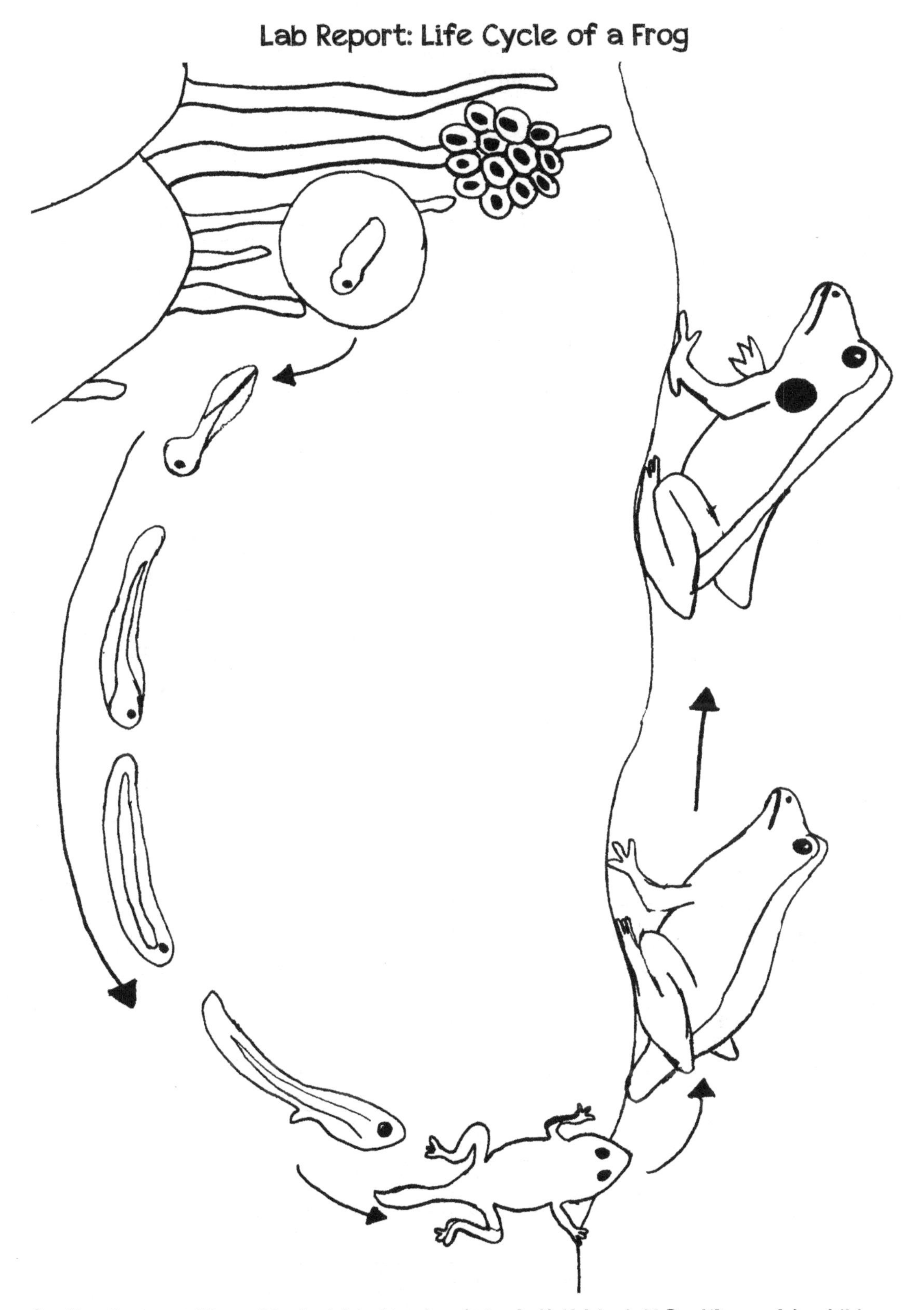

Salmon

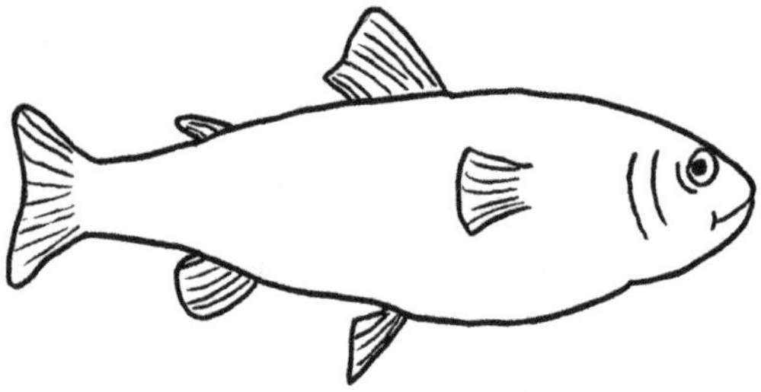

Seahorse

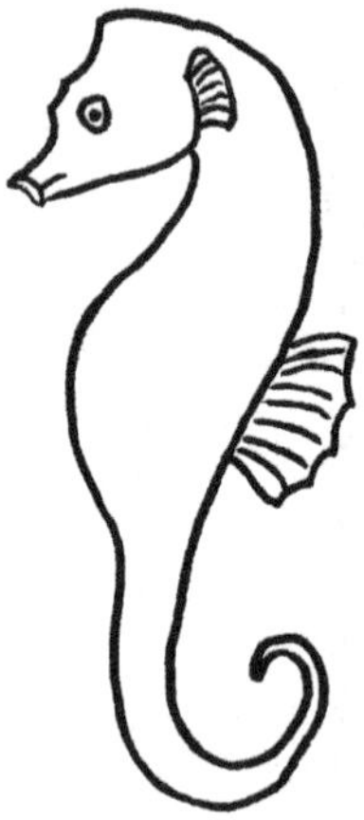

Shark

Lab Report: Equal Pressure

Our Tools

Our Method

Our Outcome

	Salty Water	Fresh Water
After 30 Minutes		
After 1 Hour		

Our Insight

Worm

Snail

Octopus

Lab Report: Holding On

Our Tools

Our Method

What it looked like

Our Outcome

Our Insight

Shrimp

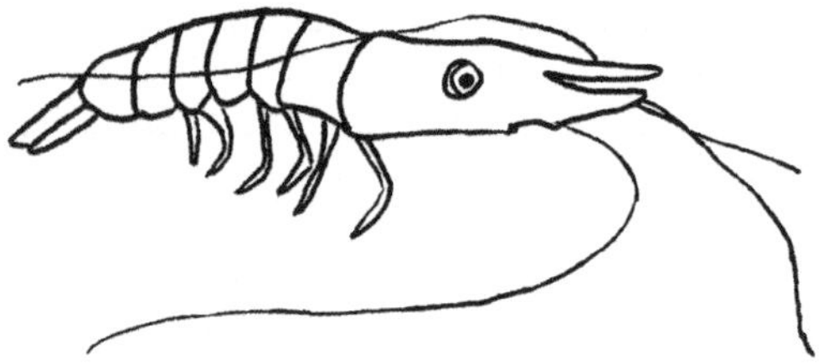

Crab

Spider

Lab Report: Telegraph Lines

Our Tools

Our Method

What it looked like

Our Outcome

Our Insight

Ant

Butterfly

Grasshopper

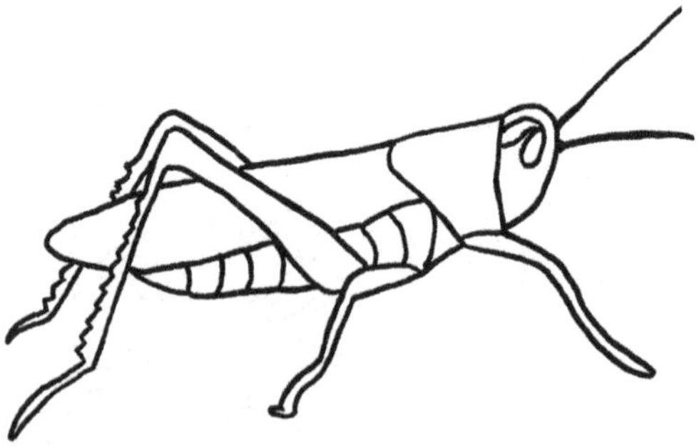

Lab Report: Butterfly Glider

What I Learned

Biology for the Grammar Stage

Human Body Unit

Human Body Unit Project

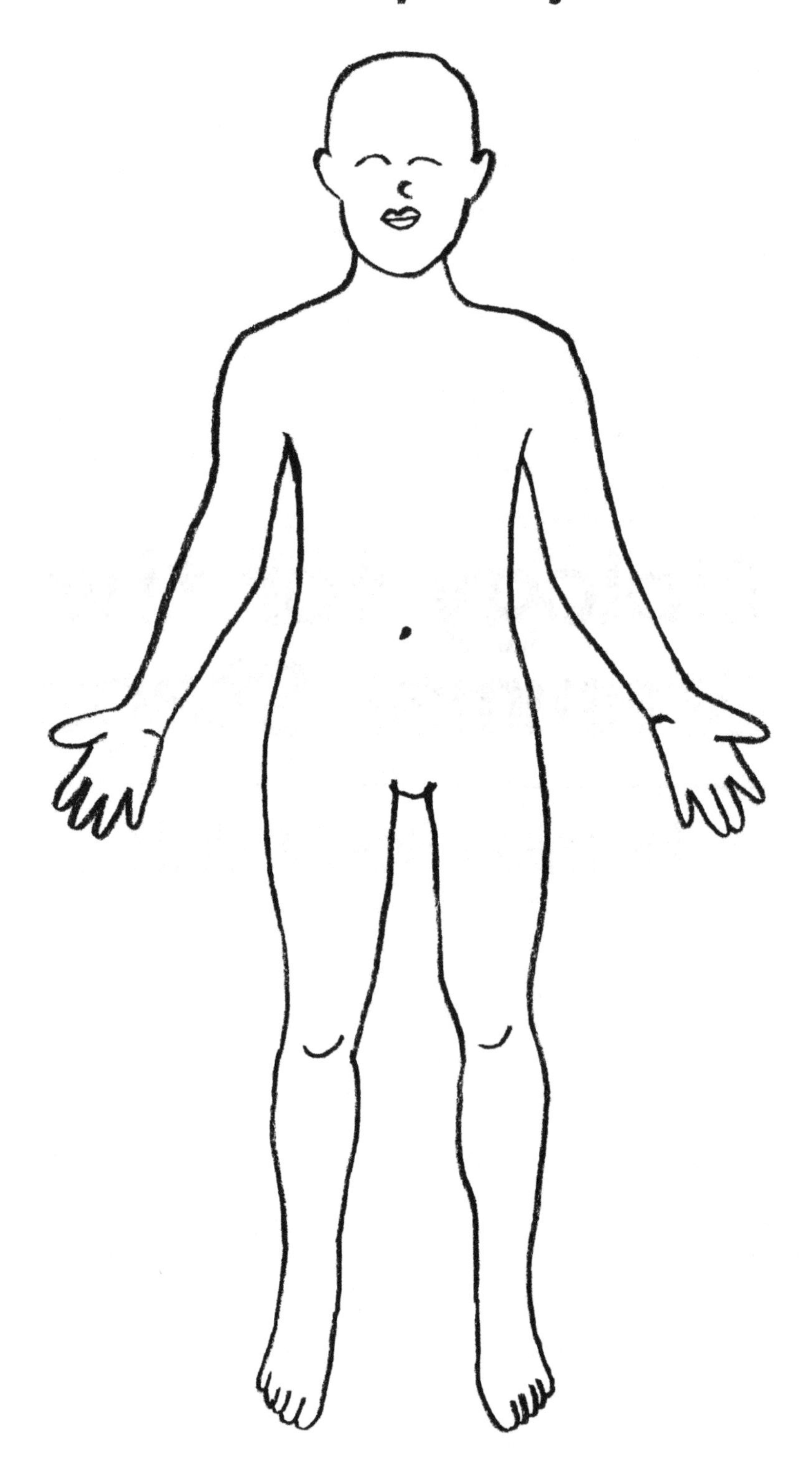

Human Body Unit Project

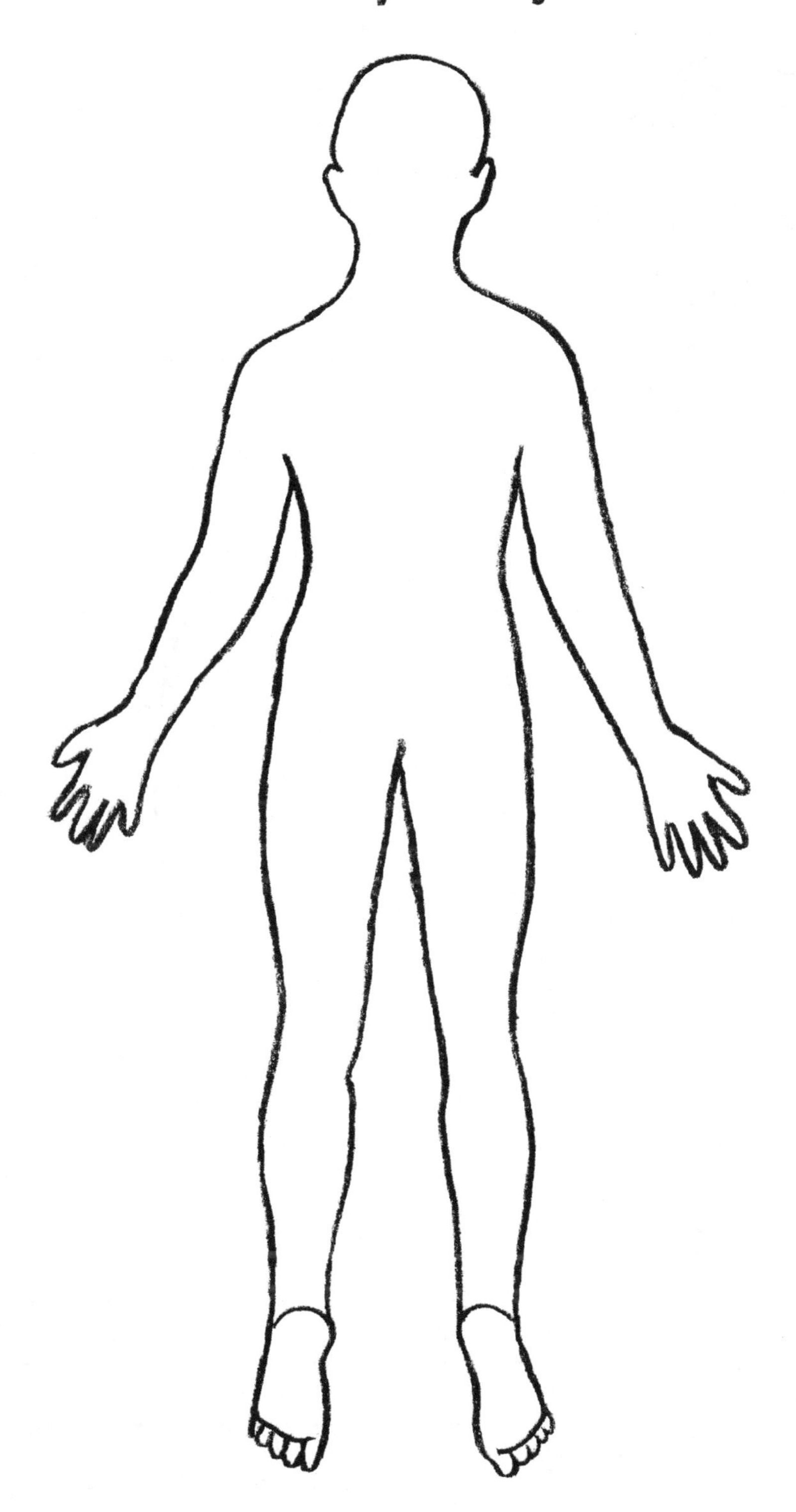

Cells

Skin

Hair

Lab Report: Fingerprints

What I Learned

Skeleton

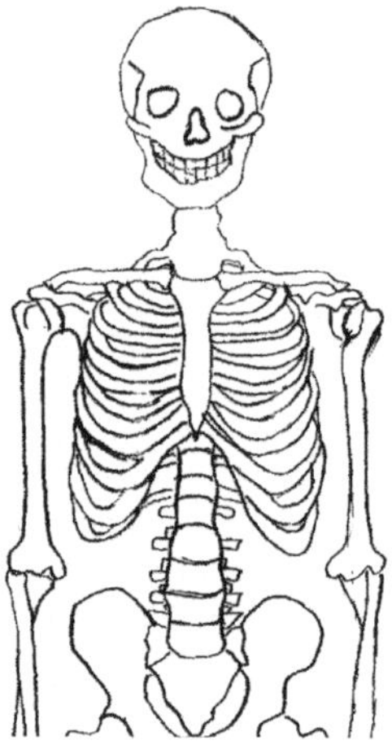

Skull

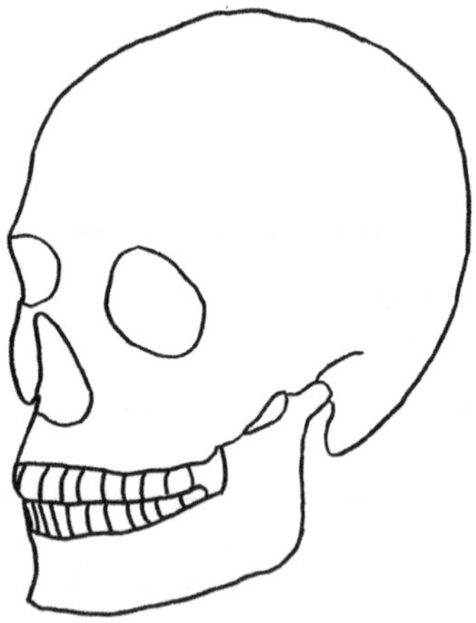

Bones

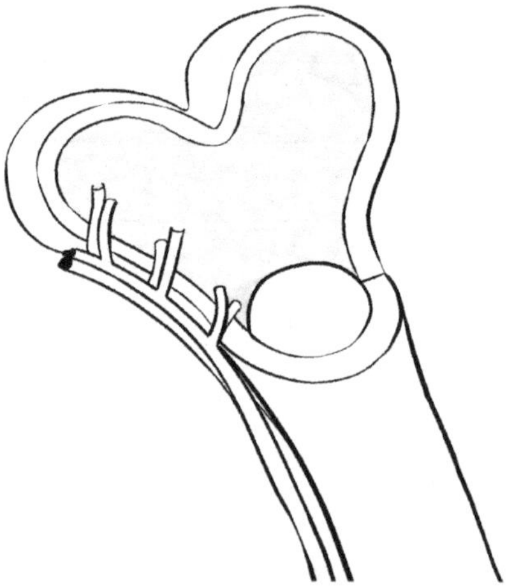

Lab Report: Soft Bones

Our Tools

Our Method

Our Outcome

Our Insight

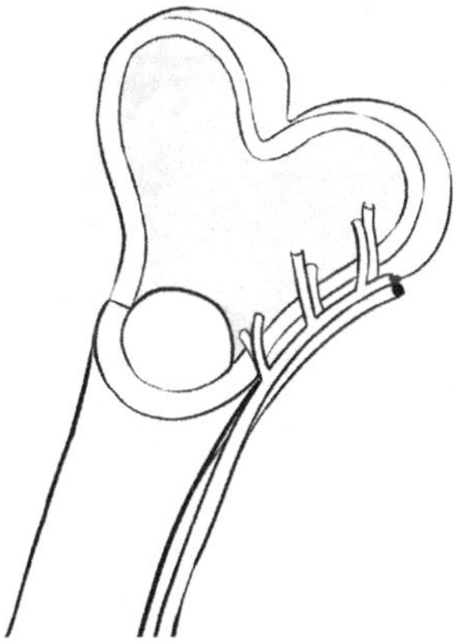

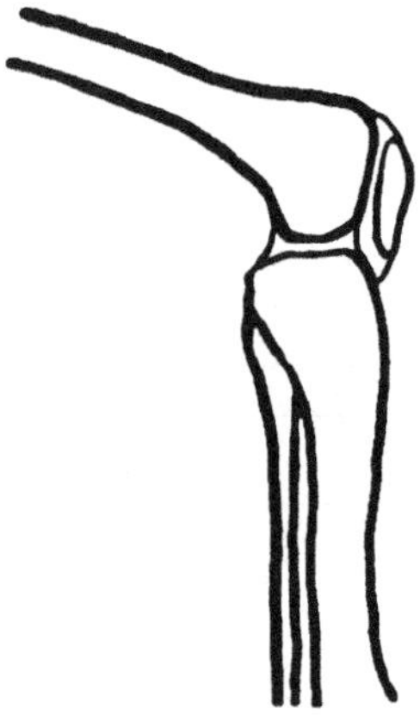

Joints

Muscles

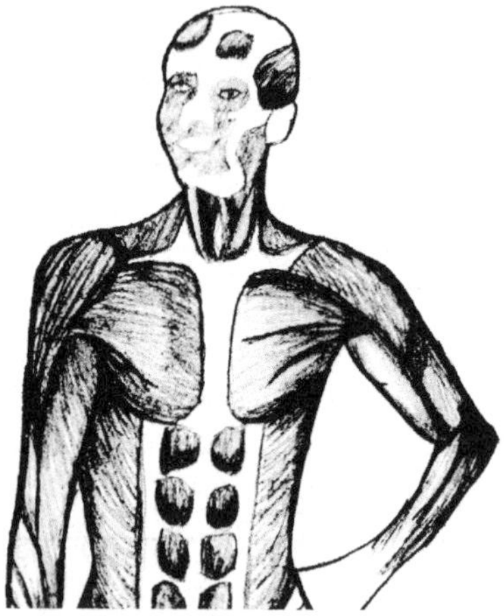

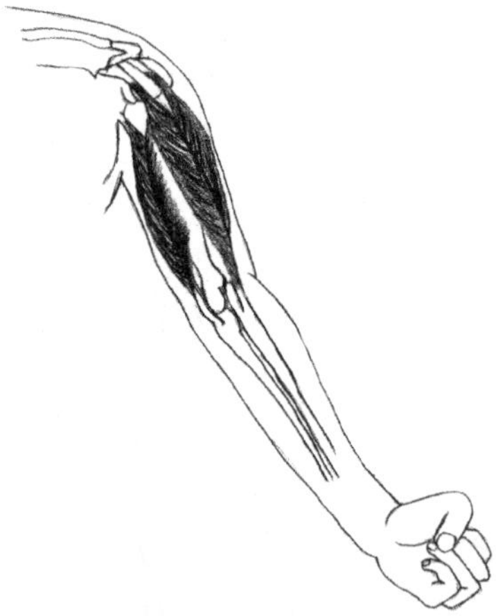

How Muscles Work

Lab Report: Muscle Strength

Our Tools

Our Method

Our Outcome

Item picked up	How hard did my muscles work?	How heavy was it?
	A little -------------------- A lot	Light Medium Heavy
	A little -------------------- A lot	Light Medium Heavy
	A little -------------------- A lot	Light Medium Heavy
	A little -------------------- A lot	Light Medium Heavy
	A little -------------------- A lot	Light Medium Heavy

Our Insight

Brain

Nervous System

Sleep

Z Z Z Z z

Lab Report: Reflexes

Our Tools

Our Method

Our Outcome

Our Insight

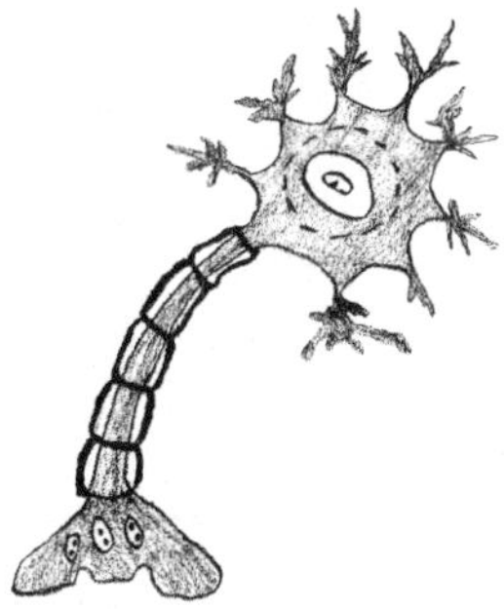

The Five Senses

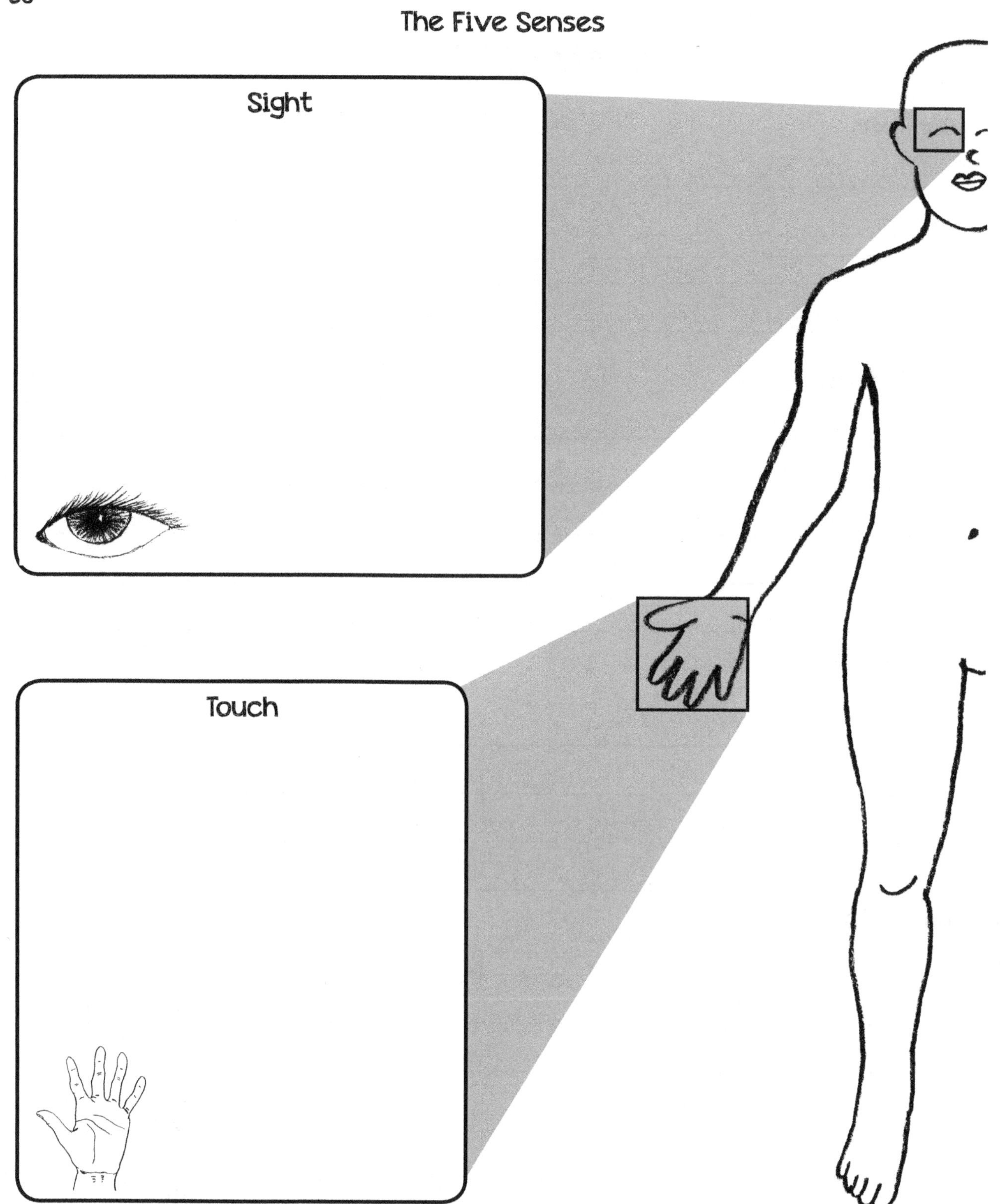

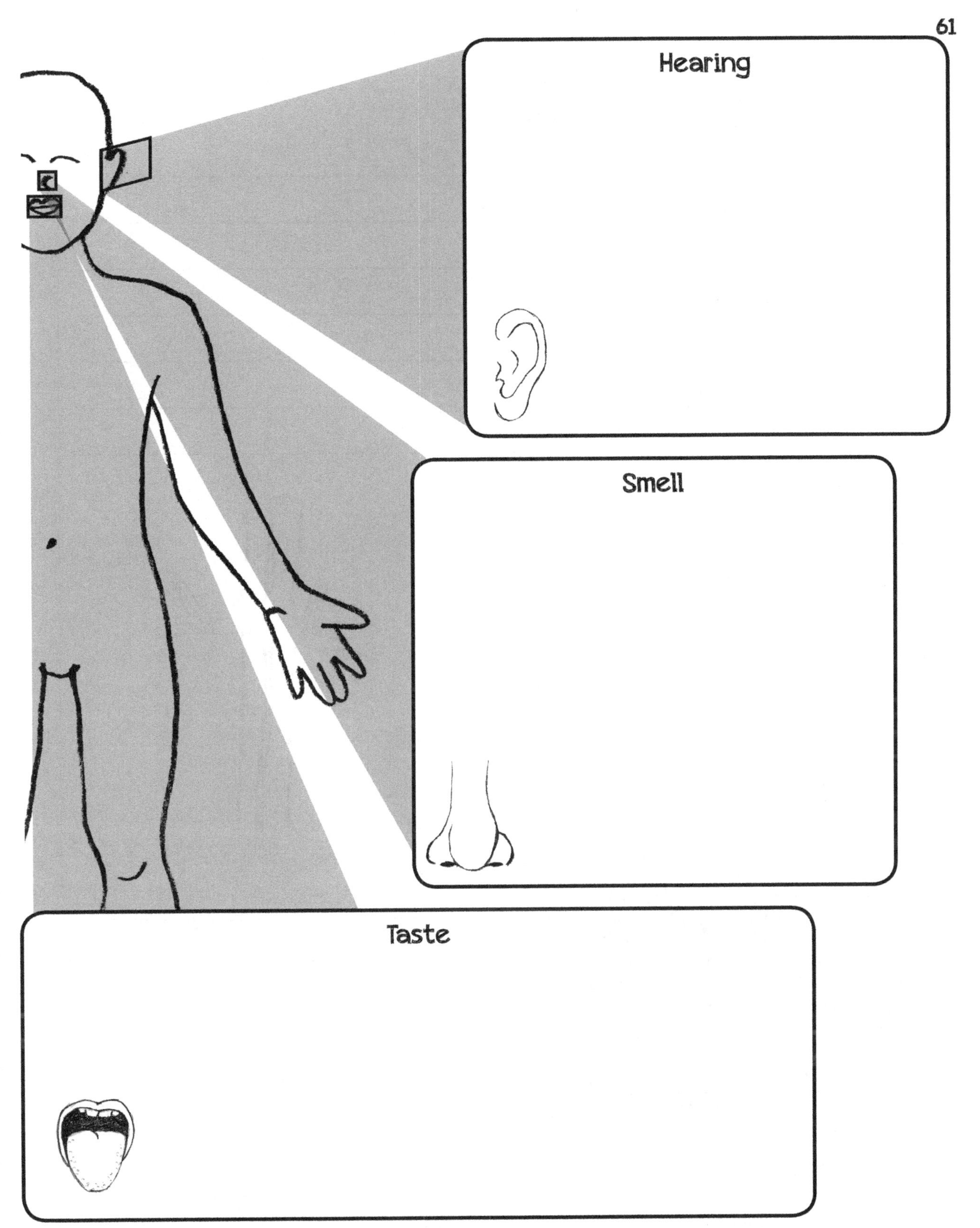
Hearing
Smell
Taste

Heart

Blood Vessels

Blood

Lab Report: Heartbeat

Our Tools

Our Method

Our Outcome

Our Insight

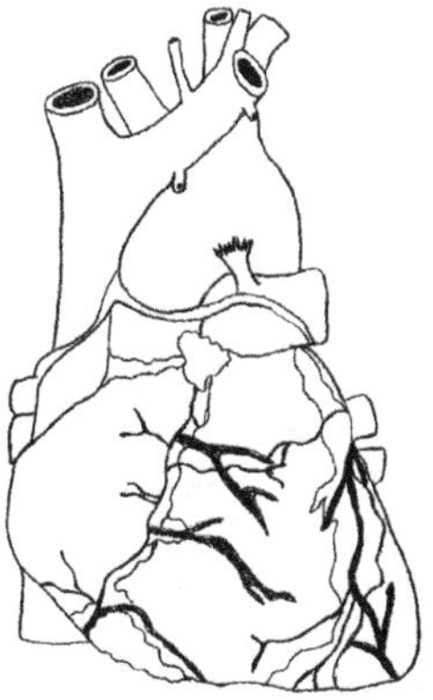

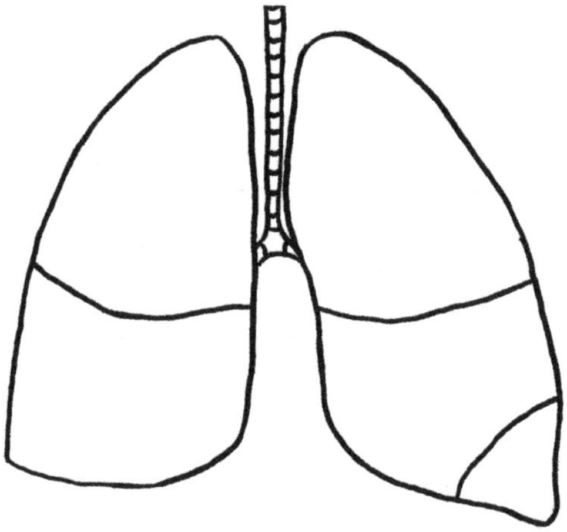

Lungs

Alveoli

Breathing

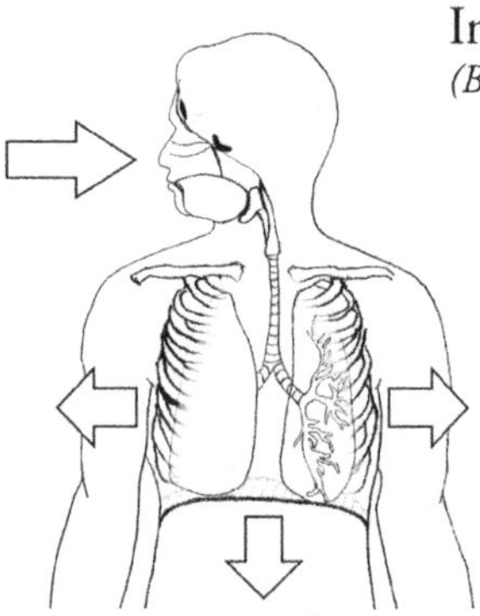

Inhalation
(Breathing In)

Lab Report: Lung Capacity

Our Tools

Our Method

Our Outcome

Our Insight

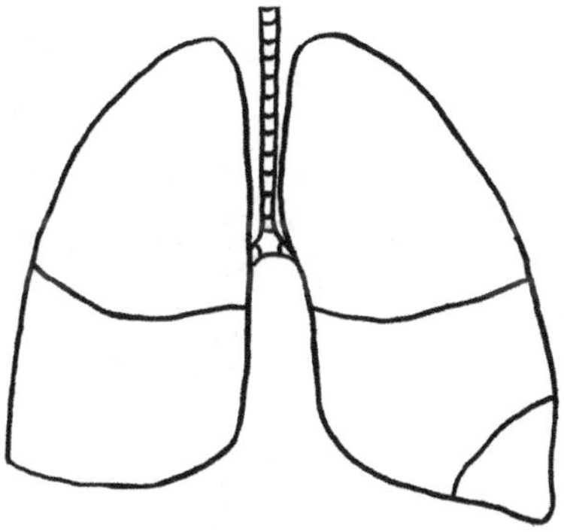

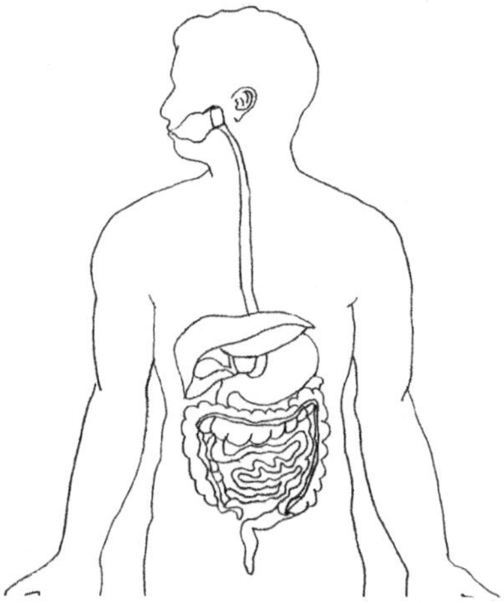

Digestive System

Teeth

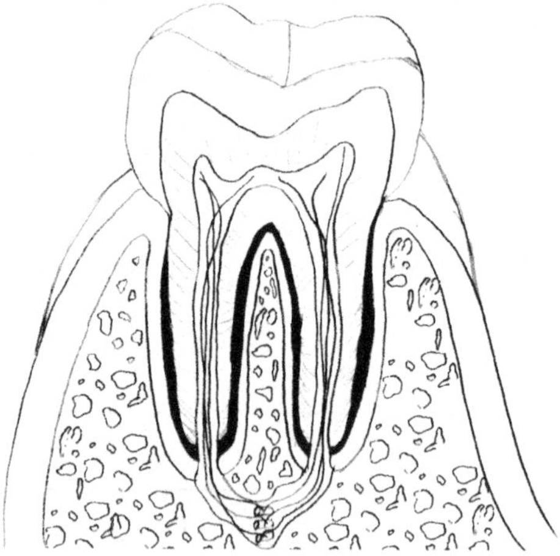

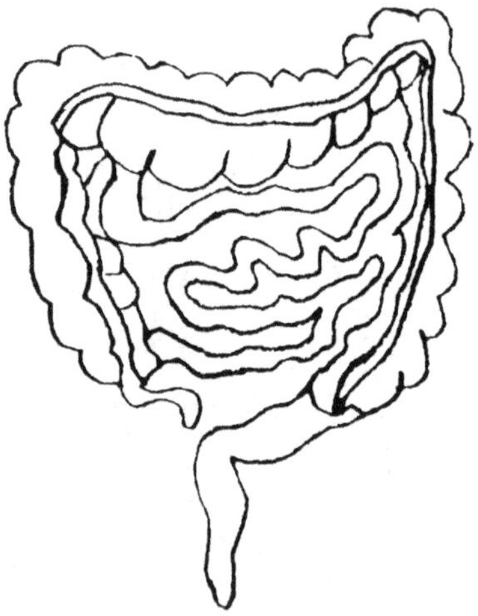

Intestines

Lab Report: Folds

Our Tools

Our Method

Our Outcome

Number of paper towels	Amount the waterline decreased
1	
3	

Our Insight

Urinary System

Bladder

Genes & DNA

My Picture Family Tree

Germs

Body Defenses

Allergies

Lab Report: Bacterial Growth

Our Tools

Our Method

Our Outcome

	Did the bacteria grow?
Warm Milk	
Cold Milk	

Our Insight

Biology for the Grammar Stage

Plants Unit

Plant Growth Chart

18						
17						
16						
15						
14						
13						
12						
11						
10						
9						
8						
7						
6						
5						
4						
3						
2						
1						
Inches	Week 1	Week 2	Week 3	Week 4	Week 5	Week 6

Leaves

Photosynthesis

Leaf Colors

Our Tools

Our Method

Our Outcome

My Results

Our Insight

Flowering Plants

Flowers

Pollen

Lab Report: Water Flow

Our Tools

Our Method

What it looked like

Our Outcome

Our Insight

Fruit

Seeds

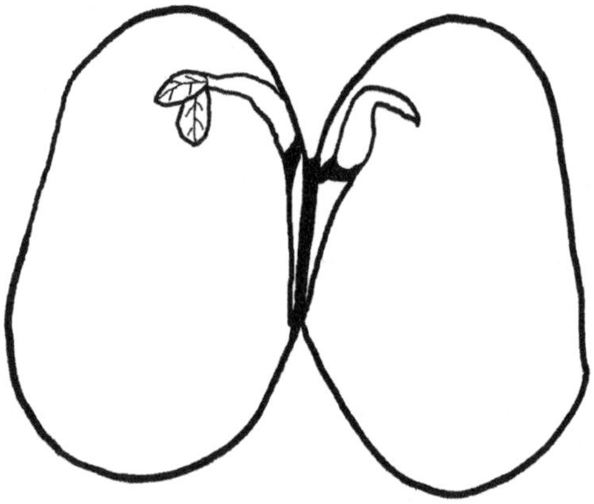

Lab Report: Baby Bean

Our Tools

Our Method

The outside of my seed	The inside of my seed

Our Outcome

Our Insight

Seedless Plants

Conifers

Fungi

Lab Report: Inside the Cone

Our Tools

Our Method

What it looked like

Our Outcome

Our Insight

Stems

Plant Cells

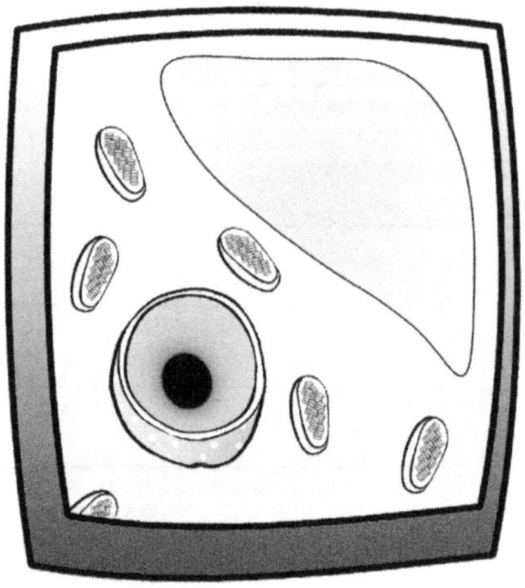

Lab Report: Stand Up

Our Tools

Our Method

Our Outcome

Our Insight

Roots

Types of Roots

Lab Report: Grow a Bean

Our Tools

______________________ ______________________

______________________ ______________________

Our Method

____

____

____

____

Our Outcome

Day	What my seeds looked like
1	
2	
3	
4	
5	

Our Insight

____

____

____

____

Biology for the Grammar Stage

Glossary

Alveoli —

Amphibian —

Bacteria —

Bird —

Blood Vessel —

Bud —

Carnivore —

Cell —

Cone —

Digestion —

Domesticated Animal —

Egg —

Fish —

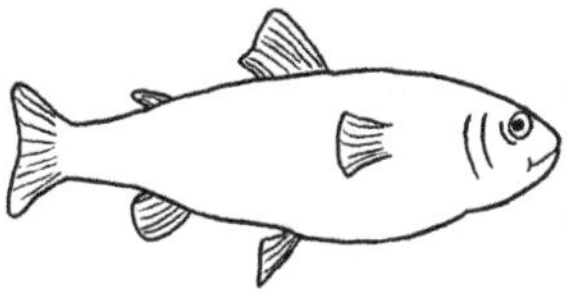

Flower —

Habitat —

Herbivore —

Insect —

Invertebrate —

Kidney —

Leaf —

Mammals —

Marine Mammal —

Migration —

Muscle —

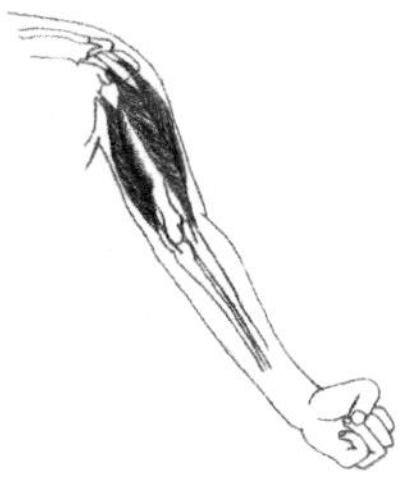

Neuron —

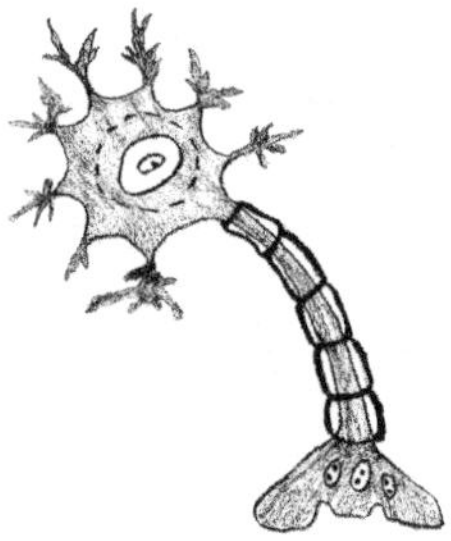

Omnivore —

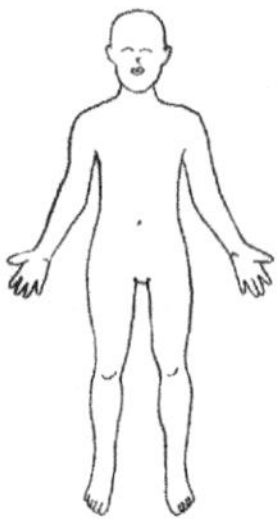

Reptile —

Roots —

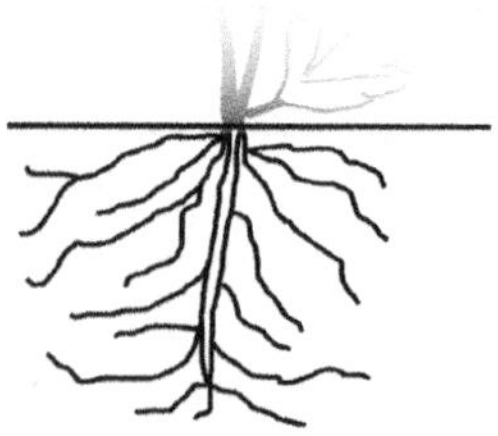

Seed —

Senses —

The Five Senses

Shellfish —

Skeleton —

Stem —

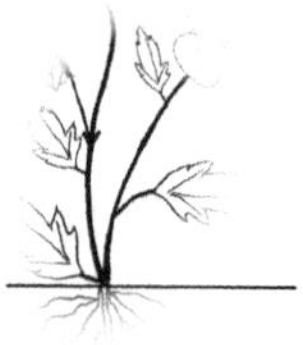

Vertebrate —

Wild Animal —

Biology for the Grammar Stage

Memory Work

Animals Unit

Characteristics of Mammals

Mammals love to breathe air
They all have fur or hair
Their blood is warm, almost hot
Their babies drink milk a lot!

Characteristics of Birds

Birds have wings
Most like to sing
They make beautiful nests
Where they lay eggs and rest

Characteristics of Reptiles

Reptiles like meat
Their blood is cold - sweet!
They have scaly, watertight skin
And in their nests their eggs lay in

Characteristics of Amphibians

Amphibians can live on water or land
They lay eggs and have cold blood - grand!

Characteristics of Fish

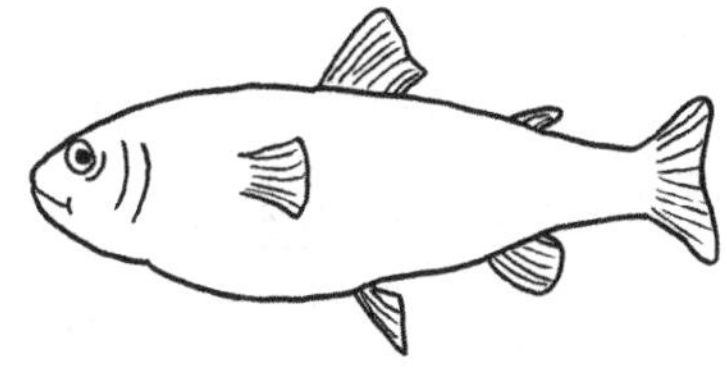

Fish swim in the sea with the otter
Using their gills to breathe in the water
They lay eggs that float through the ocean
And their strong skeletons keep them in motion.

Characteristics of Invertebrates

Invertebrates have no backbone
They live worldwide, in every zone
Ninety-seven percent of animals are in this group
Like the clams and shrimp that end up in your soup

Human Body Unit

<u>The Systems of the Human Body</u>

The skeletal system
Holds me upright

The muscular system
Moves me all night

The nervous system
Sends cells a note

The circulatory system
Keeps blood afloat

The respiratory system
Breathes in and out

The digestive system
Breaks down the trout

The urinary system
Could fill a moat

The immune system
Fixes strep throat

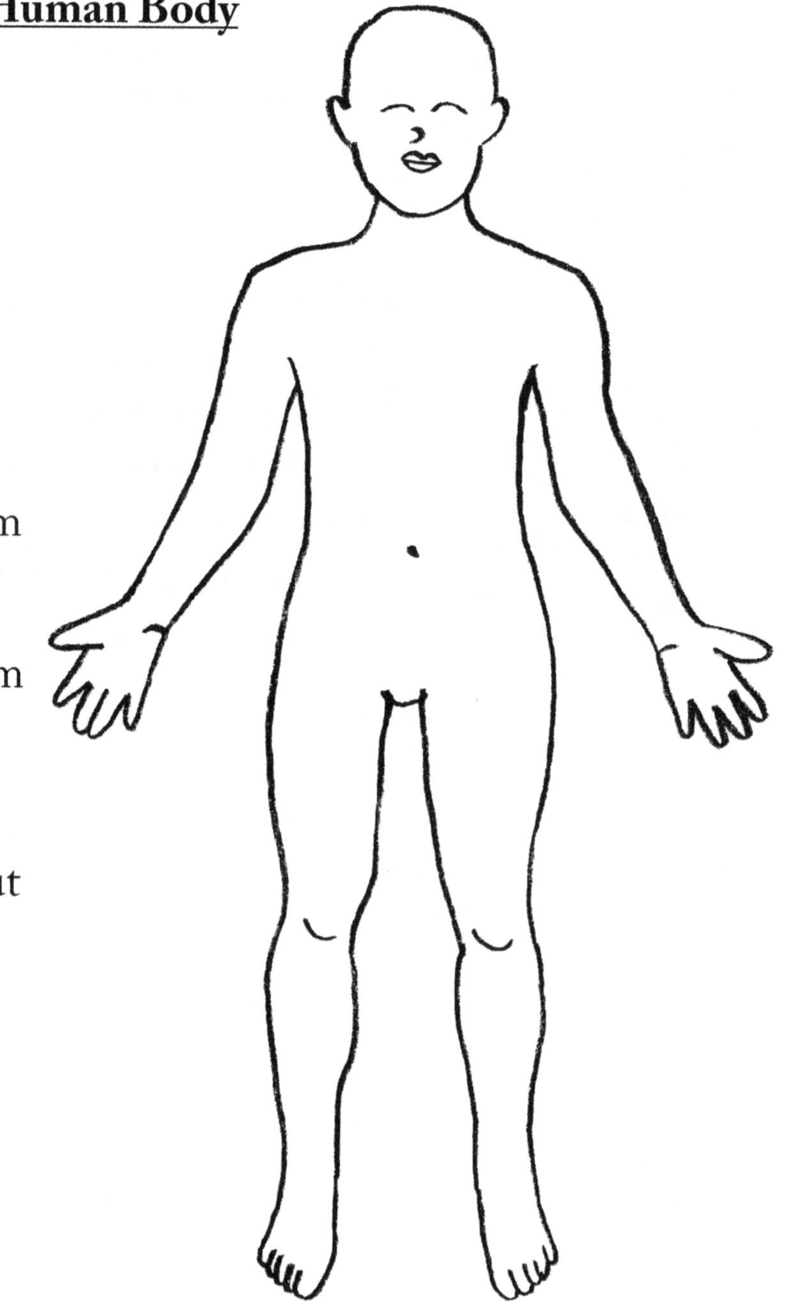

Plants Unit

Parts of a Flower

The bud becomes a flower
It's happening this very hour
The flower has petals so bright
It attracts the insect in flight
The stamen provides the pollen it needs
To join with the pistil and make a seed

Parts of a Plant

The plant stem holds it up high
The leaves reach way up to the sky
It has roots that go into the ground
Gathering nutrients and keeping balance
sound

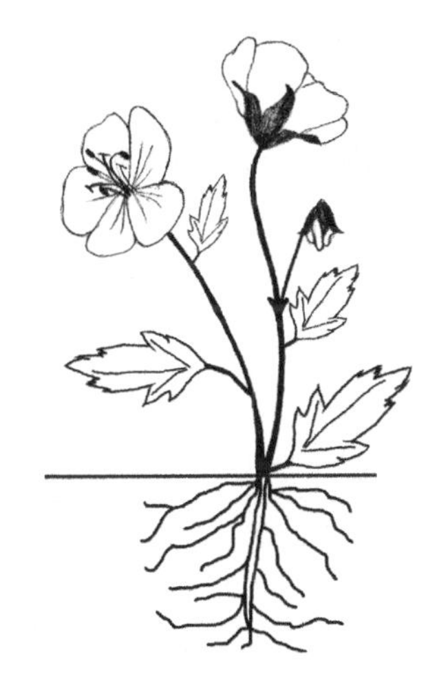

Biology for the Grammar Stage

Project Pictures

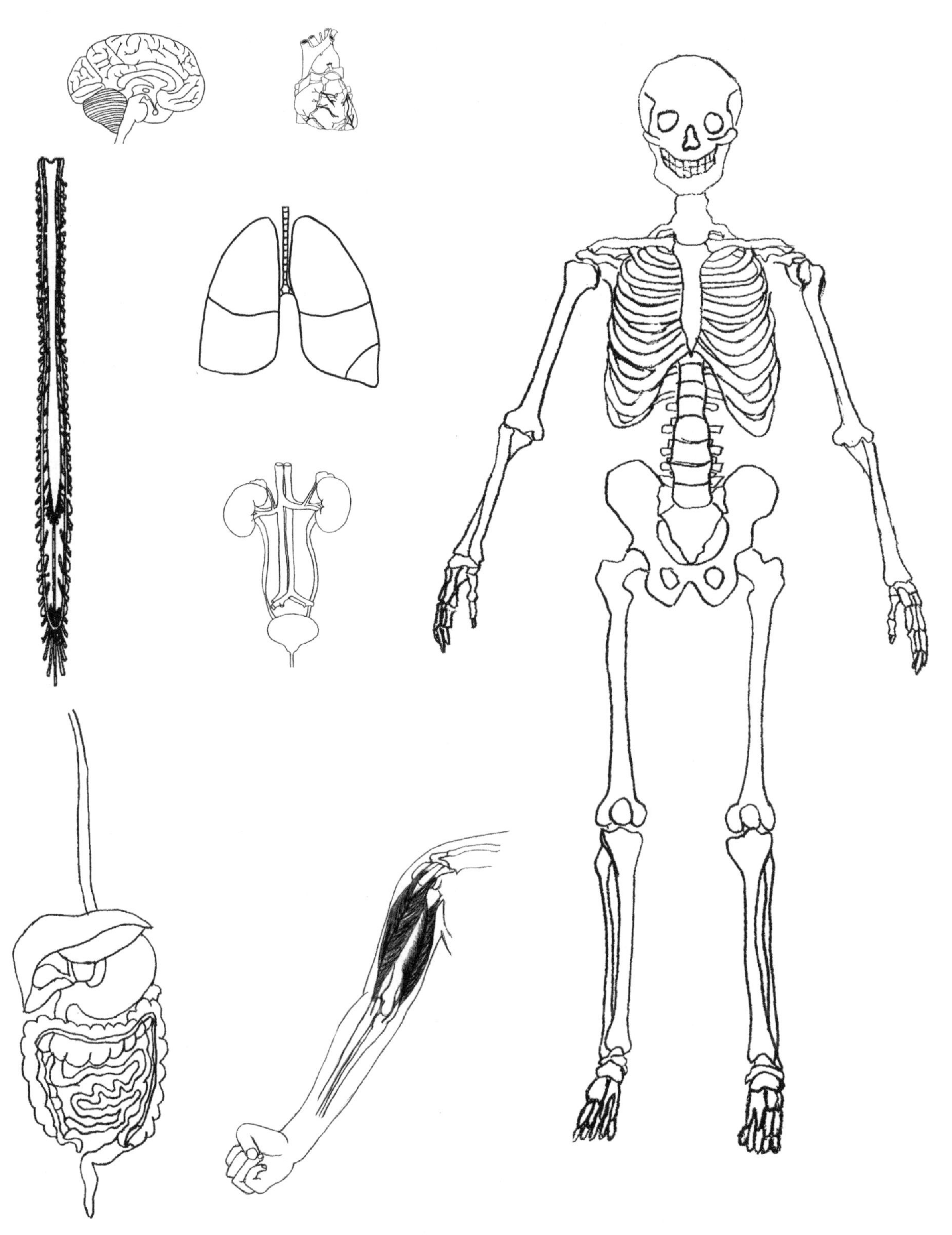

Biology for the Grammar Stage

Quizzes

Biology for the Grammar Stage Quizzes

Introduction

The following quizzes found are meant to coordinate with *Biology for the Grammar Stage*. The answers and schedule for using them are included in the teacher guide. You can use these quizzes to orally review the concepts learned or you can have the student complete one each week to test their retention of what they are learning with *Biology for the Grammar Stage*.

Table of Contents

Animals Week 1 Quiz

1. Match the following type of animal with what they eat.

Herbivore	eats both meat and plants
Carnivore	eats only plants
Omnivore	eats only meat

2. Match the following habitat with their typical characteristic.

Grassland	has lots of rain
Desert	typically very hot and dry
Rainforest	grass is the main plant

3. What is the most interesting thing you learned this week?

____

____

____

____

____

Animals Week 2 Quiz

1. **True or False:** Habitats are the natural environment of an animal.

2. The arctic habitat is typically very (hot / cold).

3. **True or False:** Animals migrate to find better living conditions.

4. Camouflage helps animals to ________________.

   run faster   hide   sleep

5. What is the most interesting thing you learned this week?

____

____

____

____

____

____

Animals Week 3 Quiz

1. **True or False:** Cheetahs run very slow.

2. Elephants are the _______________ land animals.

   lightest heaviest weakest

3. **True or False:** A group of lions that live together are called a pride.

4. Circle the characteristics of a mammal found below.

   Warm-blooded Have scales Hairy

   Their babies drink milk They have good eye sight

5. What is the most interesting thing you learned this week?

____

____

____

____

____

____

Animals Week 4 Quiz

1. **True or False:** All zebras have the same stripes.

2. Foxes have:

   Good hearing   sharp eyesight   excellent sense of smell

   All of the above characteristics

3. **True or False:** Hippopotamus means "river horse".

4. What is the most interesting thing you learned this week?

____

____

____

____

____

____

Animals Week 5 Quiz

1. Giraffe's are the world's ______________ animals.

   shortest   fattest   tallest

2. **True or False:** The male deer grows a new set of antlers each year.

3. Circle the two characteristics that help a camel's feet from sinking into the sand.

   big   small   wide   thin

4. What is the most interesting thing you learned this week?

____

____

____

____

____

____

Animals Week 6 Quiz

1. **True or False:** Chimpanzees spend most of their day on the ground.

2. Pandas eat __________ bamboo.

   a lot   a little

3. Circle where polar bears live.

   Desert   Forest   Arctic   Grasslands

4. What is the most interesting thing you learned this week?

____

____

____

____

____

____

Animals Week 7 Quiz

1. **True or False:** Young koalas like to ride on their mother's backs.

2. Beavers use their long __________ to cut down trees to make their homes.

   tails   claws   teeth   hair

3. Circle two things that kangaroos use when they jump.

   strong back legs   a nice breeze

   long tails   big nose

4. What is the most interesting thing you learned this week?

____

____

____

____

____

____

Animals Week 8 Quiz

1. **True or False:** Armadillos have armor.

2. Rabbits can have ___________ babies each year.

   a few   some   a lot

3. **True or False:** Skunks spray a very nice scent for defense.

4. What is the most interesting thing you learned this week?

____

____

____

____

____

____

Animals Week 9 Quiz

1. Whales are the _______________ creatures that live on Earth.

   smallest biggest funniest

2. **True or False:** Walruses have a thick layer of fat to keep them warm.

3. Dolphins are ___________ intelligent sea mammals.

   not sort of very

4. What is the most interesting thing you learned this week?

____

____

____

____

____

____

Animals Week 10 Quiz

1. Male cows are called __________.

    boys   cows   bulls

2. **True or False:** Goats are good climbers.

3. Pigs like to eat ___________.

    peanut butter   anything   hay

4. What is the most interesting thing you learned this week?

____

____

____

____

____

____

Animals Week 11 Quiz

1. Circle all the characteristics of a bird.

Lays eggs Warm-blooded Hairy

Has feathers Drinks milk

2. **True or False:** Parrots live in cold places with little Sun.

3. **True or False:** Owls hunt mainly at night.

4. **True or False:** Eagles are good hunters because of their strong wings and sharp eyesight.

5. What is the most interesting thing you learned this week?

____

____

____

____

____

____

Animals Week 12 Quiz

1. **True or False:** Chickens can be found all over the world.

2. Ducks normally live ________________.

   in caves   on the land   in the water

3. Circle two things that help to keep a penguin warm.

   Waterproof feathers   Nice smile

   Heater   Layers of fat

4. What is the most interesting thing you learned this week?

____

____

____

____

____

____

Animals Week 13 Quiz

1. Hummingbirds are tiny birds whose wings beat ______________.

   very slow   at normal speed   very fast

2. **True or False:** Swans have long necks.

3. Swallows work ______________ to build mud nests.

   alone   together

4. What is the most interesting thing you learned this week?

____

____

____

____

____

____

Animals Week 14 Quiz

1. **True or False:** Male peacocks are much more colorful than female peacocks.

2. Ostriches lay ____________ eggs.

   small   average-sized   giant

3. **True or False:** Flamingos get their pink color from the water that they stand in.

4. What is the most interesting thing you learned this week?

____

____

____

____

____

____

Animals Week 15 Quiz

1. Circle all the characteristics of a reptile.

   Cold-blooded   Warm-blooded

   Lays eggs   Has rough skin

2. **True or False:** Chameleons cannot change their color.

3. **True or False:** Iguanas have spines running along their backs.

4. **True or False:** Rattlesnakes don't make a noise.

5. What is the most interesting thing you learned this week?

____

____

____

____

____

____

Animals Week 16 Quiz

1. **True or False:** Amphibians are cold-blooded animals with smooth skin.

2. **True or False:** Frogs and toads are not amphibians.

3. Turtles have soft bodies that are protected by ______________.

   bones a heavy shell rubber

4. **True or False:** Crocodiles like to sunbathe.

5. What is the most interesting thing you learned this week?

____

____

____

____

____

____

Animals Week 17 Quiz

1. Circle all the characteristics of a fish.

Smooth skin   Cold-blooded   Has gills

Hairy   Covered with scales

2. **True or False:** Salmon always swim downstream.

3. **True or False:** Baby seahorses live in their daddy's tummies before they are born.

4. **True or False:** Sharks find their prey by smell.

5. What is the most interesting thing you learned this week?

____

____

____

____

____

____

Animals Week 18 Quiz

1. Invertebrates are animals ____________ backbones.

   with without

2. **True or False:** Worms dig their way through the soil by eating it.

3. Snails live ________________________.

   only on land only in the water both on land & in water

4. Octopuses have ______ arms, called tentacles.

   4 6 8 10

5. What is the most interesting thing you learned this week?

____

____

____

____

____

____

Animals Week 19 Quiz

1. **True or False:** Shellfish are aquatic animals without shells.

2. Crabs have two front __________ to help them get food & fight off attackers.

   spears   hands   pinchers

3. **True or False:** Shrimps live in oceans, rivers and lakes.

4. Spiders have ______ legs.

   4   6   8   10

5. What is the most interesting thing you learned this week?

____

____

____

____

____

____

Animals Week 20 Quiz

1. Insects have (1 3 5) body parts and (4 6 8) legs.

2. **True or False:** Grasshoppers can make noises by rubbing their legs together.

3. **True or False:** Butterflies turn into caterpillars through metamorphosis.

4. **True or False:** Ants live together in colonies.

5. What is the most interesting thing you learned this week?

____

____

____

____

____

____

Human Body Week 1 Quiz

1. Your body has _____________ of cells.

   a few   a couple hundred   billions

2. Circle the two layers of skin.

   Dermis   Prodermis   Epidermis

3. **True or False:** Hair is alive and hurts when you cut it.

4. What is the most interesting thing you learned this week?

____

____

____

____

____

____

Human Body Week 2 Quiz

1. Circle all the things that your skeleton does.

Glows in the dark — Supports your body

Allows you to move — Protects certain organs

2. Your skull protects your ____________.

stomach — toes — brain — lungs

3. **True or False:** Bones contain the mineral calcium which helps make them strong.

4. What is the most interesting thing you learned this week?

____

____

____

____

____

____

Human Body Week 3 Quiz

1. Muscles are controlled by your ______________.

   mouth brain fingers

2. Muscles ______________ to make the bones of my body move.

   push contract

3. **True or False:** Joints help your body to move.

4. What is the most interesting thing you learned this week?

____

____

____

____

____

____

Human Body Week 4 Quiz

1. A ______________ is a nerve cell that carries electrical messages.

   cell neuron muscle

2. **True or False:** The brain is not a part of the nervous system.

3. **True or False:** I need sleep.

4. What is the most interesting thing you learned this week?

____

____

____

____

____

____

Human Body Week 5 Quiz

1. Match the body parts to the sense that uses it.

Nose	Sight
Ear	Hearing
Eye	Taste
Skin	Smell
Tongue	Feel

2. **True or False:** My senses help me gather information about the world around me.

3. What is the most interesting thing you learned this week?

____

____

____

____

____

____

The Five Senses

Human Body Week 6 Quiz

1. The heart ____________ blood through the body.

    climbs pumps runs

2. The ____________ carry blood through the body.

    blood vessels bones muscles

3. **True or False:** Red blood cells carry white blood cells.

4. What is the most interesting thing you learned this week?

____

____

____

____

____

____

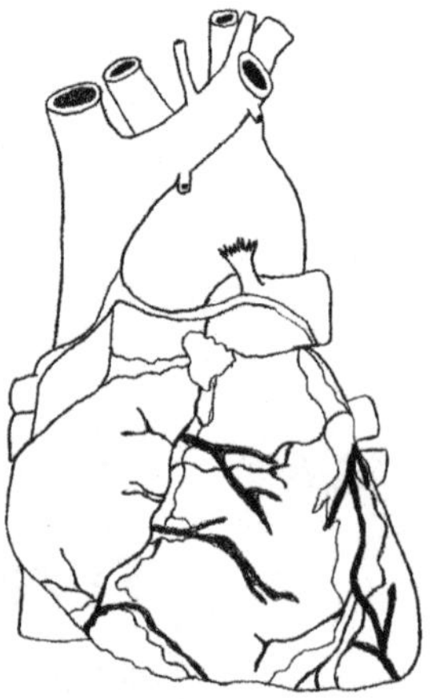

Human Body Week 7 Quiz

1. **True or False:** The lungs take in air.

2. The lungs give (oxygen carbon dioxide) to the blood and remove (oxygen carbon dioxide) from the blood.

3. **True or False:** Alveoli are tiny air bags found in your brain.

4. What is the most interesting thing you learned this week?

____

____

____

____

____

____

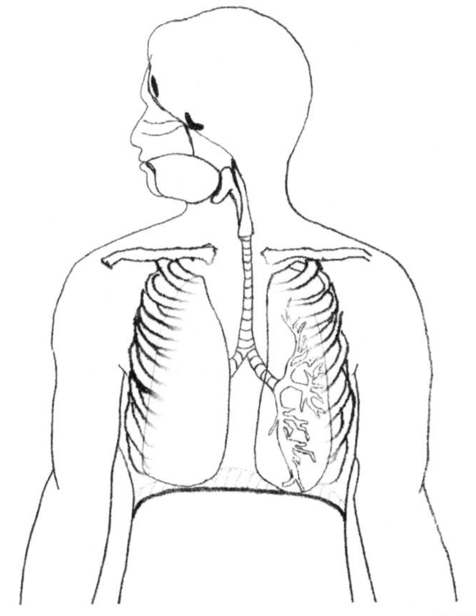

Human Body Week 8 Quiz

1. Digestion is the process by which your food is ________________.

    put back together   broken down

2. __________________ help to chew up your food.

    Your heart   Your teeth   Your eyes

3. **True or False:** The large intestine absorbs water.

4. What is the most interesting thing you learned this week?

____

____

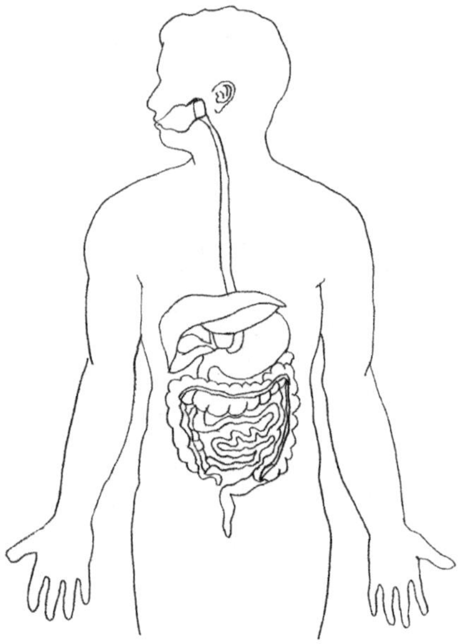

____

____

____

____

Human Body Week 9 Quiz

1. **True or False:** Your bladder can't stretch.

2. Your kidneys get rid of _____________.

   blood   air   waste

3. **True or False:** Genes help to determine what we will look like.

4. What is the most interesting thing you learned this week?

____

____

____

____

____

____

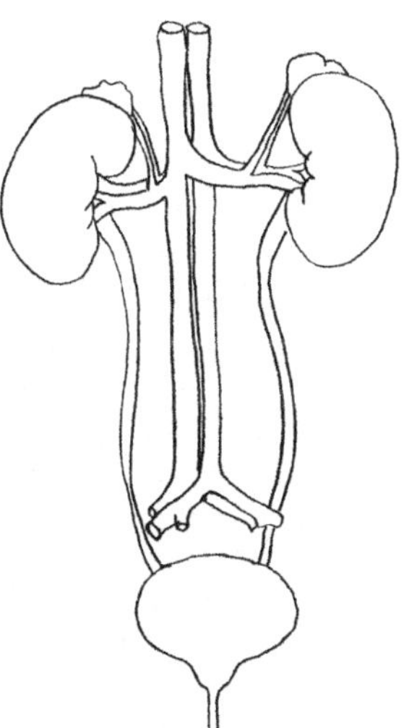

Human Body Week 10 Quiz

1. **True or False:** Bacteria is what causes you to get sick.

2. Germs are ______________.

   microscopic   big   banana-sized

3. My body's defense system is called the ______________ system.

   digestive   circulatory   immune

4. What is the most interesting thing you learned this week?

   ____

   ____

   ____

   ____

   ____

   ____

Plants Week 1 Quiz

1. A ______________ is the part of the plant that makes the food.

leaf stem flower

2. Circle the name of the process where light energy is turned into food for a plant.

respiration photosynthesis churning

3. **True or False:** Chlorophyll is able to absorb sunlight.

4. What is the most interesting thing you learned this week?

____

____

____

____

____

Plants Week 2 Quiz

1. **True or False:** Pollen is made in the male parts of the flower and fertilizes the \ female parts of the flower.

2. Circle all of the things flowers do for the plant.

   Produce seeds   Attract insects

   Are the reproductive part of the plant

3. **True or False:** All flowers are the same size.

4. What is the most interesting thing you learned this week?

____

____

____

____

____

____

Plants Week 3 Quiz

1. **True or False:** Seeds contain a baby plant.

2. Fruits help to ________________ seeds.

   protect   disperse   protect & disperse

3. Plants have fruit to ______________.

   move seeds   look pretty   have something to eat

4. What is the most interesting thing you learned this week?

____

____

____

____

____

____

Plants Week 4 Quiz

1. Cones are ________________ produced by conifers.

   dry fruits   needles   leaves

2. **True or False:** Spores are tiny copies of seedless plants.

3. Circle all the fungi.

   Ferns   Mushrooms   Yeasts   Moss   Molds

4. What is the most interesting thing you learned this week?

____

____

____

____

____

____

Plants Week 5 Quiz

1. Circle all the things the stem does for the plant.

Holds up flowers | Supports the plant

Transports food & water | Makes food

2. Label the following items on the plant cell below - cell wall, nucleus, and chloroplasts.

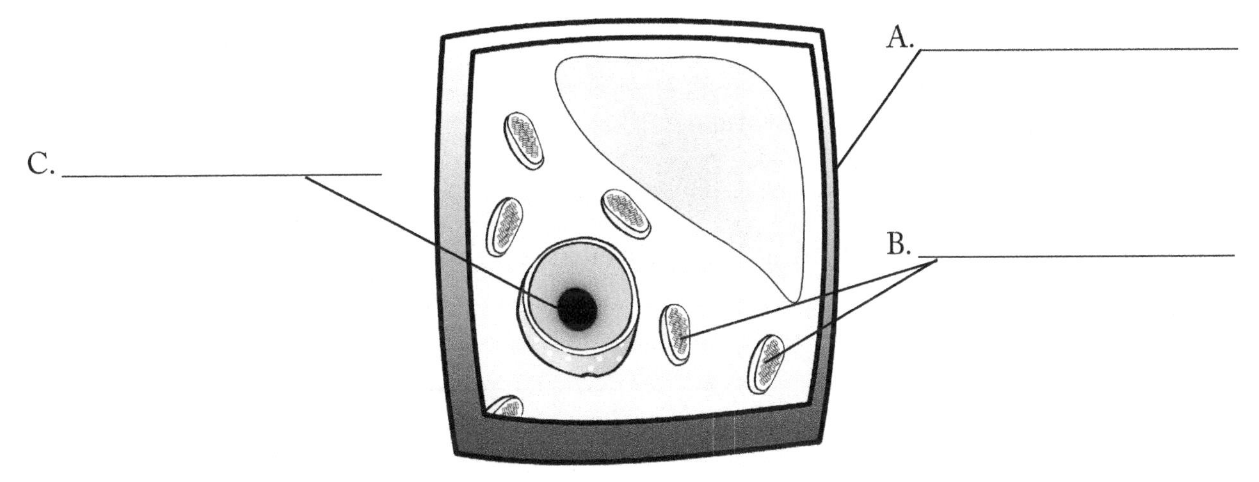

3. What is the most interesting thing you learned this week?

____

____

____

____

____

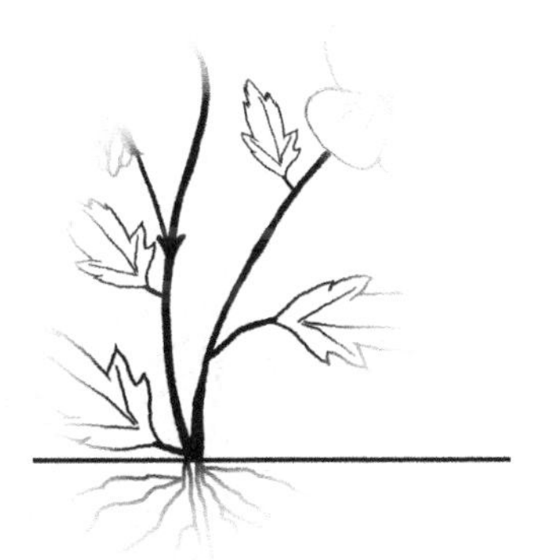

Plants Week 6 Quiz

1. Match the type of root to what it does.

   fibrous root   grows down

   taproot   grows out

2. **True or False:** Roots suck up water and nutrients from the soil.

3. Roots help to make the plant ___________.

   weak   strong

4. What is the most interesting thing you learned this week?

____

____

____

____

____

____

99103992R00085

Made in the USA
Columbia, SC
09 July 2018